Bringing Up Father

BRINGING UP FATHER ® by GEOMCMANUS

STARRING
MAGGIE and JIGGS

Edited by HERB GALEWITZ
Designed by DON WINSLOW

Charles Scribner's Son's • New York

Copyright © 1973 King Features Syndicate, Inc.

*This book published simultaneously in the
United States of America and in Canada—
Copyright under the Berne Convention*

*All rights reserved. No part of this book
may be reproduced in any form without the
permission of Charles Scribner's Sons.*

1 3 5 7 9 11 13 15 17 19 MD/C 20 18 16 14 12 10 8 6 4 2

Printed in the United States of America
Library of Congress Catalog Card Number 73-5190
SBN 684-13544-2

We wish to thank John H. Wright of King Features Syndicate for his cooperation in the preparation of this collection.

CONTENTS

INTRODUCTION

If you're looking for a descriptive term for "Bringing Up Father," try "gemütlichkeit," the German word for a warm, happy, comfortable family feeling. At first glance, this might seem strange. After all, the main recurring action of the comic is Jiggs's attempts to spend his evenings with the "boys" at Dinty Moore's instead of at home with wife Maggie. But it's true. And despite Maggie's bombardment of Jiggs with vases and rolling pins, the feisty couple really were in love with each other, and in moments of dire distress they would openly confess their feelings. The reading public also joined this love-fest, by making "Bringing Up Father" one of the most successful and enduring comic strips of all time.

At its height, the comic was read daily and Sunday by millions of people in the United States and forty-six other countries, where it was translated into sixteen languages. Naturally, there were adjustments. In Finland, it was known as "Victor and Klara"; in Denmark, "The Golden Kick"; in France, "The Family Next Door"; and in literal Poland, "Dzygs I Megi." As for corned beef and cabbage, the changes to fit the varied national appetites were: England— tripe and onions; China— fish and rice; France— beef stew; Turkey— beefsteak and cabbage; and Italy— stewed codfish.

At the turn of the century, corned beef and cabbage was an inexpensive staple of the poor Irish workingman. McManus recalled that in his native St. Louis in the 1890s, twenty cents worth of corned beef and cabbage could provide a family of four with an ample dinner.

In real life, McManus had to suffer for his celebration of corned beef and cabbage. At every public occasion and many private ones, well-meaning hosts were sure to serve heaping platters of the savory stuff. At one time, McManus liked the dish, but under the deluge his taste buds soured and he had the temerity to turn down New York Mayor La Guardia's offering with the lame excuse that he was going on a diet. McManus did not like French or Italian food either. He preferred American cooking and plenty of it, so that his five-foot, three-inch frame eventually expanded to the point where he had to cut his Sunday pages in half in order to reach the top strips at the drawing board.

The inspiration for "Bringing Up Father" goes back to St. Louis where George McManus was born on January 23, 1884. George's Irish-born father was the manager of the St. Louis Opera House. There young George saw several performances of *The Rising Generation,* a play starring a popular Irish actor, Billy Barry. The play revolved around a newly rich Irish family and their difficulty in adjusting to their changed station in life. Seventeen years later, McManus recalled this play while searching for a new comic strip idea and made it the basis for "Bringing Up Father." The first daily strip appeared January 2, 1913, in Hearst's *New York American* and quickly became a success.

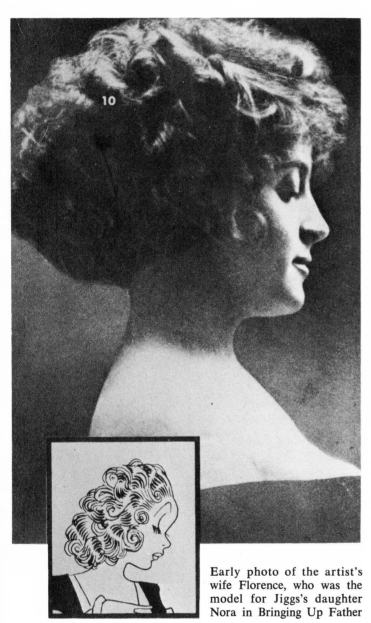

Early photo of the artist's wife Florence, who was the model for Jiggs's daughter Nora in Bringing Up Father

Inspiration for Jiggs was Billy Barry, an actor whom McManus recalled seeing as a youngster in St. Louis

McManus's newspaper career began in St. Louis after an abbreviated high school education. It seems that fifteen-year-old George had been sent home for drawing pictures during a class lecture. Instead of the expected thrashing, the elder McManus took the drawings to the editor of the St. Louis *Republic* newspaper and obtained a job for his son as janitor and messenger boy at five dollars a week. In due time, George worked his way up to staff artist where he sketched enough hangings (a hundred and twenty) and suicide victims to last him a lifetime. His salary was still meager, but he managed extra income by moonlighting for Anheuser Busch. The work consisted of going around to various saloons and ordering his employer's product in a loud and clear voice. He was finally rescued from these morbid and belt-busting jobs by an omnipotent bootblack who gave him a tip on a thirty-to-one horse. Impulsive George placed a hundred dollars on Hamburg Belle running at Belmont Park. The horse won, and with three thousand dollars in his pocket McManus quit his jobs and the next day headed for New York.

After six months of unsuccessful job hunting combined with high life in Bagdad on the Hudson, the bankroll had dwindled to point zero. At that time, McManus received two offers on the same day, one from McClure's *Syndicate* and the other from Pulitzer's *New York World*. McClure's offered the larger salary, but as the *World* had an outlet in St. Louis, McManus chose the latter. He wanted to show the hometown folks that he was doing good.

McManus's comic creations for the *World* included "Nibsy the Newsboy in Fairyland," "Panhandle Pete," "Snoozer," "The Ready Money Ladies," "Let George Do It" (which became a stock phrase), "Spare Ribs and Gravy," and "The Newlyweds and Their Baby," among others. The latter comic became his most successful and attracted the attention of William Randolph Hearst. In the fashion of those days, Hearst offered McManus a considerable raise in salary to join the *New York American* and he accepted. The title had to remain with the *World,* so George McManus renamed the strip "Their Only Child."

In the early days, Jiggs had a goatee which made him look like a stage Dutch comic; it was soon discarded. A lantern jaw disappeared in the 1920s, and a "dese and dose" vocabulary was also corrected at the same time. Apparently, Maggie's relentless attempt to "improve" Jiggs's appearance in high society did bring results. He was less prone to sit around the house in his undershirt and socks, and switched from smoking an Irish clay pipe to cigars. Some of these changes were made to avoid a dated look as the stage Irishman and Dutch comic disappeared from theaters. Also, the burly, former hod carrier Jiggs was softened to create a better contrast to the bellicose Maggie. Initially Maggie was quite buxom, but she soon slimmed down.

This was dictated by the swinging of fashion's pendulum from an ample Anna Held to the slender Ziegfield Girl. Maggie was always style conscious and her wardrobe is an excellent guide to women's fashions for five decades.

Daughter Nora inherited her mother's penchant for being a clotheshorse; a beautiful Gibson Girl face (McManus claimed that his wife Florence was the model); sensational legs that McManus was prone to exhibit; and a placid, vapid mind. With all these attractions, Nora could allure only equally vapid, but silly looking Englishmen as suitors. In fact, she married one of these Lords and went off to live with him. Later, Nora returned to the strip and no further mention was made of her husband. The Jiggs family was discreet.

Maggie and Jiggs also had a son, Sonny. He was a collegiate nitwit much in the vein of Arthur Lake's film roles. Sonny, who was far from handsome, surprised one and all by bringing home a beautiful bride who promptly went to work to support him. Later, they presented Maggie and Jiggs with their only grandson, Jiggie. The name was concocted in a "name the baby" contest. Soon after, the Sonny family disappeared from the strip and was no longer seen or mentioned.

Dinty Moore, Jiggs's favorite restaurateur, was *not* based on New York restaurant owner James Moore. The latter actually believed that McManus, who was a steady customer of his, was poking fun at him. But McManus had borrowed the name Dinty from a boyhood bellhop friend and added Moore because they seemed to go together. When it finally dawned on James Moore that the publicity was of great value, he changed the name of the restaurant to Dinty Moore and became a close friend of McManus. He even permitted McManus to take down his chandeliers, pull them apart, and put them together again. This hobby, along with collecting canes and toy trains, was McManus's main diversion after his seven-day-a-week labor on "Bringing Up Father." McManus claimed never to have taken a vacation, though in the last twenty years of the strip he was assisted by Zeke Zekley.

However, McManus was well compensated. His income from newspaper syndication alone reached two thousand dollars a week. Add to this the proceeds from the toys and games based on his characters, book collections that sold in the millions, and a half-dozen or so films, some of which he appeared in, and a stage production that toured the hinterlands for a dozen years. When he lost his first fortune in the 1929 crash, he calmly went home and started on his second one. McManus was generous to a fault. He advised that the best way to get rid of peddlers and borrowers was to pay them immediately and be done with them.

Essentially, "Bringing Up Father" is a two-character comic, with two major themes, the social climbing of Maggie and the determination of Jiggs to be with the boys. For forty-two years, until his death in 1954, McManus evoked endless variations on these ideas. As the years rolled on, the audience became intimately acquainted with every nuance of Maggie and Jiggs. They weren't flat characters, but real people whom we knew very well. The comic withstood fantastic changes in taste and style through eras that would be almost incomprehensible to each other. Obviously, Maggie and Jiggs concerned themselves with something basic to mankind. Whether it was simply the relationship of husbands and wives or just men and women, we are not sure, but we do know that "Bringing Up Father" was one of the greatest comic strips.

Herb Galewitz

George McManus in 1923. He started as newspaper artist for old St. Louis Republic at age of 14, later switched to the New York World and was hired by Hearst publications in 1910

Spare Ribs and Gravy...Early McManus' Comics

Early McManus' Comics...The Newlyweds

The Newlyweds ... Early McManus' Comics

Bringing Up Father...

Circa 1916-17

Father Is Taking No Chances

Father's Daughter Is a Practical Person

Father Is What You Call An Optimist

Father Doesn't Worry Over Trifles

Father's Friend Is a Poor Sailor

Father Thinks There Will Be No Other Lesson

Father Doesn't Understand Society People

Father Has a Close Shave

Circa 1916-17

Father May Bring Back a Necklace. Also May Not

Father Has a Long Memory

Father Changes His Stand

Father Grasps The Idea

Father Likes To Stay Home—Sometimes

Father Knows a Good Man When He Sees Him

Father Takes No Chances

Father Proves He's Right

Circa 1916-17

Father Does Not Commit Himself

Father Finds It Costs To Live

Father's Beard Grows Quickly

Father Stays Home

Father Learns From Experience

Father Loves Nature

Father Is Willing To Move

Father Needs a Rest

Circa 1916-17

Father Is a Creature of Habit

Father Makes a Grand Break

Father Gives Out Information

Father May Have Stopped Running

1919 ... Bringing Up Father

And Daughter Ought to Know.

Oh, There are Other Ways.

Oh, Most Decidedly Tardy!

Ah, Yes, She Loves her Father.

Father Gets an Awful Jolt.

Where a Little Foresight Helps.

Why Clancy Was Sore.

How Shells Often Travel.

1919 ... Bringing Up Father

The BRINGING UP FATHER *Game*

| For 2, 3 or 4 players. In Bright Colors. Spinners, Markers, Directions. | Latest, most delightful home game for children and grown-ups. | Refined and Rollicking. Easy to learn, Hard to quit. Impossible to beat. | You can get on "Ha! Ha!" "Hooray!" "Ouch!" "Outa Luck!" and "Home James!" |

Send $1.50 to the Embee Distributing Company
141-155 East 25th Street, New York City, N. Y.
We pay the parcel post and insure it.   And there you are!

1919 . . . Bringing Up Father

Father Really Needs Exercise.

Father Is Willing to Pay.

Father Didn't Use A Knife, Anyway.

Father Thinks It Better To Give Than Receive.

Bringing Up Father...1919

Father Thinks Maggie Is Unreasonable.

Father Certainly Has A Kind Heart.

Father Now Has A New Habit.

Father Didn't Recognize The Hat.

1921 ...Bringing Up Father

Bringing Up Father

1921...Bringing Up Father

Father Has Good Judgment.

Father Is Willing To Oblige.

Father Was Never In Africa.   ### Father Now Understands It.

Bringing Up Father...1921

Father Tries To Satisfy Maggie.

Father Decides To Get Insured.

Father May Forget, At That.

Father Almost Got Into Trouble.

1921 ... Bringing Up Father

Father Is Interested In Medicine.

Father's Courage Oozes Out.

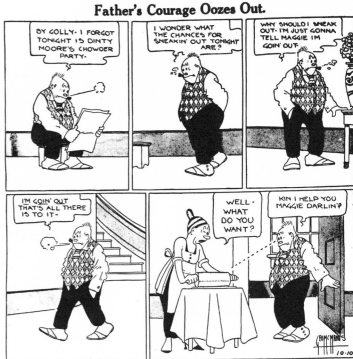

Father Cuts His Work Short.

Father Spoils The Scenery.

Father Meets Mrs. Smith's Daughter.

Father Is Crazy About Corned Beef.

Father May Prove An Alibi—Maybe.

Father Finds A Familiar Sign.

1921 ... Bringing Up Father

1924 ...Bringing Up Father

Bringing Up Father ... 1924

1924 ...Bringing Up Father

© 1930, Int'l Feature Service, Inc., Great Britain rights reserved.

1929 ...Bringing Up Father

Bringing Up Father ... 1929

1929 ... Bringing Up Father

1929 ... Bringing Up Father

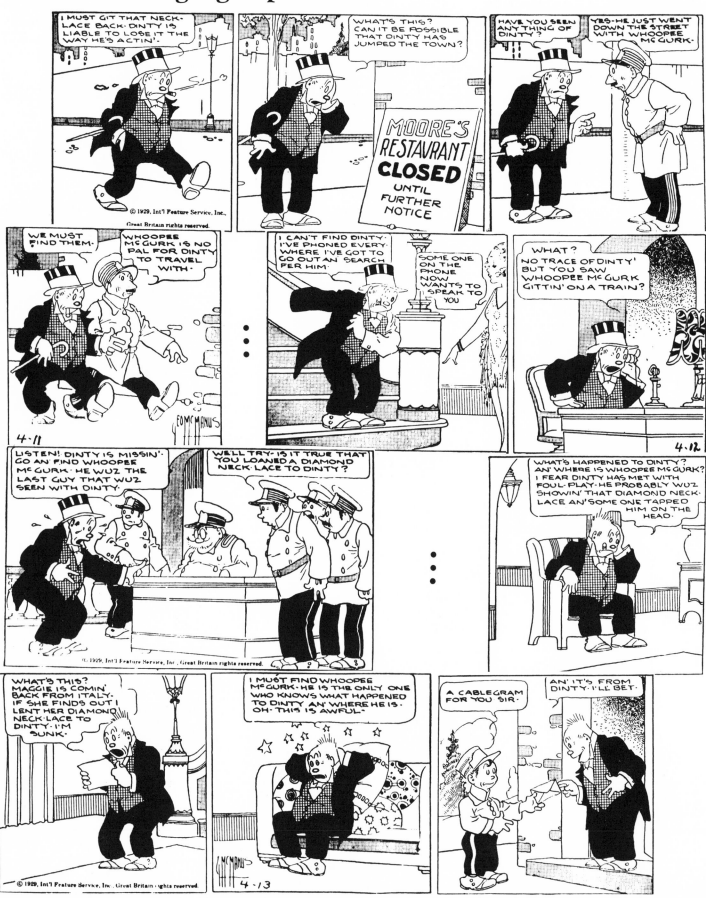

Bringing Up Father ... 1929

41

1929 … Bringing Up Father

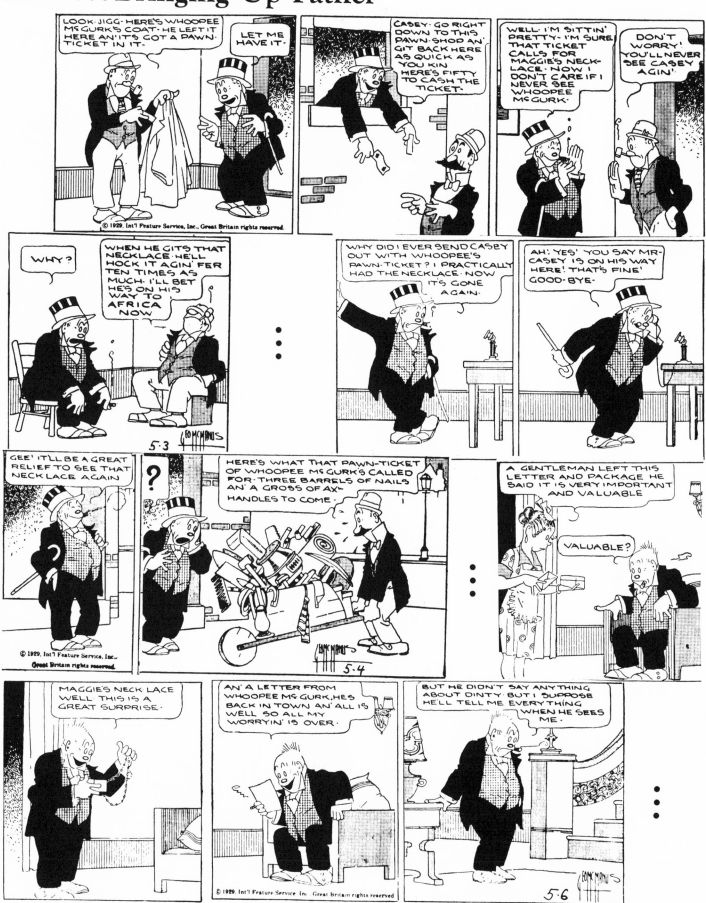

1930 ... Bringing Up Father

1935...Bringing Up Father

1935...Bringing Up Father

REMEMBER, MAGGIE, THE DAY YOUR MOTHER GAVE 'WILLIE A DIME TO CLEAN THE ATTIC WHERE YOUR FATHER USED TO TAKE HIS DAILY NAP- AND NIP-

AND TOM MANJERRY'S IDEA OF LIFE WAS A CHAIR IN TH' KITCHEN NEAR A WINDOW-A FAN-A BUCKET-A DIME AND SOMEONE TO GO AFTER IT-

1-16

AND HOW WE KIDS ENVIED JERRY McGUIRE WHEN HE HAD THE MUMPS AN' DIDN'T HAVE TO GO TO SCHOOL-

AND YOUR UNCLE BINNY WHO WAS A FLAGMAN AT TH' RAILROAD YARDS- AND ON HIS DAY OFF HE WOULD SPEND IT WITH TH' MAN WHO TOOK HIS PLACE-

AND WHEN TH' BRANIGANS WENT ON A PICNIC YOU'D THINK THEY WERE MOVING OUT OF TOWN- THE ONLY LOAD THEY'D BRING BACK WAS THEIR FATHER-

AND YOUR FATHER WAS ALWAYS WAITING FOR "CEMENT-HEAD" PARAFFIN, THE TOWN DUDE TO SAY JUST ONE WORD SO HE'D HAVE AN EXCUSE TO HIT HIM-

1-12

AND THE DAY YOUR AUNT CAME HOME AND FOUND THAT THE CAT HAD EATEN THE TROUT YOUR UNCLE HAD MOUNTED ON A BOARD-

AND HOW WE KIDS LIKED TO GO UP ON THE ROOF AND WAIT FOR THE FIGHT TO START OVER THE PINOCHLE GAME IN DUGAN'S BACK-YARD-

AND THE DAY WE HAD OUR PICTURE TAKEN AND WE GAVE YOUR DAD ONE- AND HE WANTED TO KNOW WHY-

1937 ... Bringing Up Father

1937...Bringing Up Father

AND REMEMBER DANNY DUGAN - HE SPENT SO MUCH TIME LOOKING IN PICTURE - MACHINES HE ALWAYS LOOKED LIKE HE WAS WINKING—

AND THE STYLE THOSE THEATRICAL MANAGERS WOULD PUT ON WHEN THEY CAME TO TOWN—

A ROOM WITH RUNNING WATER-

AND THE DAY MAZIE HAZEY ELOPED SHE RAN AWAY WITH HY WATTERS, THE ANT-EXTERMINATOR - FOUR WEEKS LATER HE RAN AWAY FROM HER—

REMEMBER HOW THE OLD AWNING QUARTETTE USED TO SING ON THE CORNER - NOW THEY ARE ALL IN SING-SING—

AND THE MULLIGAN KIDS USED TO DRESS UP ON SUNDAY - IF KIDS WORE RED TIES LIKE THEY DID IN THOSE DAYS - WE WOULDN'T NEED TRAFFIC SIGNALS—

YOUR UNCLE WAS ALWAYS LOOKING FOR TOUGH GUYS - AND WHEN HE WOULD SEE ONE YOUR UNCLE WOULD DISAPPEAR—

AND HOW PROUD YOU WERE WHEN I TOOK YOU UP ON TH' AVENUE AN' WE MINGLED WITH THE ELITE—

AND HOW COLD IT WAS, GETTING UP IN THE MORNING - WE USED TO GET THE ICE-PICK TO BREAK THE ICE IN THE WATER-PITCHER SO WE COULD WASH—

1937 ... Bringing Up Father

1937...Bringing Up Father

1937 ... Bringing Up Father

1937 . . . Bringing Up Father

1937...Bringing Up Father

1938 ... Bringing Up Father

1938...Bringing Up Father

JIGGS, I WANT YOU TO HURRY HOME. THERE ARE SOME OF THE CHILDREN FROM THE OLD NEIGHBORHOOD HERE

I'LL GO RIGHT HOME. IT WILL BE GOOD TO SEE THEM

3·12

HELLO, DARLING

WHO'S THE BOZO?

HELLO, FALSE FACE

NOW THE WHOLE DAY IS SPOILED

SIC, IM, PRINCE

DON'T TURN AROUND NOW WHATEVER YOU DO

IF I COULD ONLY CONVINCE MAGGIE TO MOVE BACK INTO THE OLD NEIGHBORHOOD-

HAVE NO FEAR- YOU'LL HAVE TO CONVINCE HER GRADUALLY-

I'VE GOT DUGAN WORKIN' ON IT RIGHT NOW - HE IS GOING TO PUT THINGS AROUND YER HOUSE AN' IN YER GARDEN THAT WILL REMIND HER OF THE OLDEN DAYS - AN' IT'LL SOFTEN HER HEART-

SWELL-

EEK-

GOOD GRACIOUS- MRS JIGGS- YOU HAVEN'T TURNED YOUR BEAUTIFUL ESTATE INTO A BEER GARDEN- HAVE YOU - ?

DINTY MOORE.

3·14

OSMOND- TAKE THIS PICTURE IN TO MRS. JIGGS-AN' TELL HER I SENT IT IN- AN' DO NOT ANSWER ME BY SAYIN' "YES-ME LORD".

YES -ME LORD--

WHEN SHE SEES THAT PICTURE OF THE OLD HOUSE IN THE GOOD OLD NEIGHBORHOOD-- SHE'LL GIT A LONGIN' TO MOVE BACK THERE- I HOPE-

3·15

YES - I RECOGNIZED THE OLD HOME - BUT IT HAS DETERIORATED SO - HOW ANYONE COULD LIVE IN SUCH AN UNKEPT OLD PLACE IS BEYOND ME - WHO IS THAT FOOL MAN AND THAT FILTHY- LOOKING WOMAN ON THE PORCH ?

THIS PICTURE WAS TAKEN TWENTY YEARS AGO --- THAT'S 'HORSECAR' CASEY- THE MOTORMAN THAT MARRIED YER COUSIN SARAH- THAT'S HER SITTIN' BESIDE HIM - THEY MOVED IN JUST AFTER WE LEFT---

?

OH! HOW I MISS THE OLD GANG OF MINE-

AH- THAT SURE BRINGS TEARS TO ME EYES - I'D GIVE ME ALL TO BE BACK IN THE GOOD OLD STREET WITH ME PALS OF YEARS GONE BY-

BY GOLLY- I'LL GO AND DIG UP TH' OLD QUARTETTE THAT USED TO SING ALMOST EVERY SATURDAY NIGHT AT MAGGIE'S HOUSE- I'LL GET THEM TO SING AGIN' FOR HER -

3·16

YOU SAY THEY'RE NOT AROUND -

NO- FINNIGAN- DOYLE AND FLARRETY ARE IN JAIL AN' TH' COPS ARE LOOKIN' FER DUGAN-

1938 ... Bringing Up Father

97

1938 ... Bringing Up Father

1938 ... Bringing Up Father

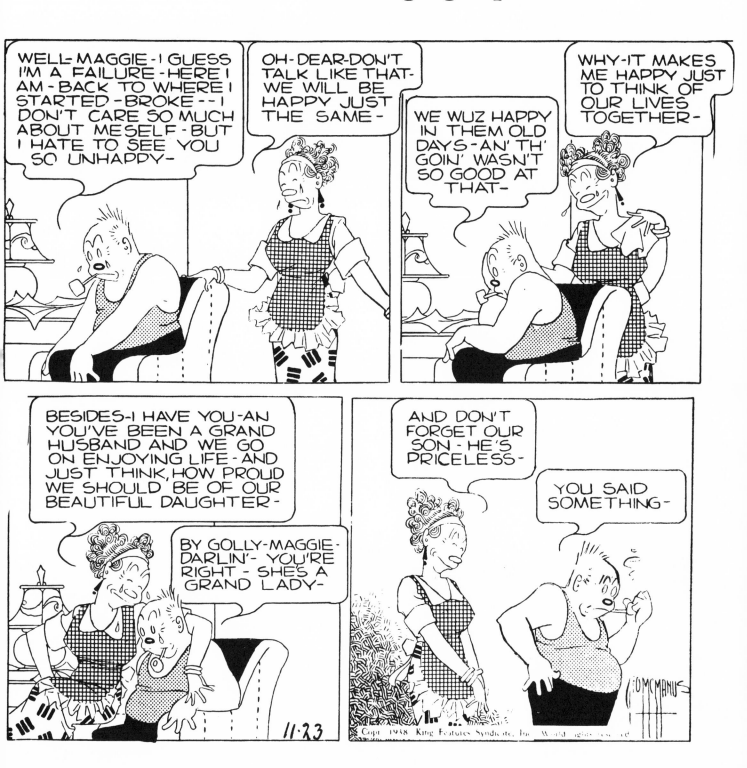

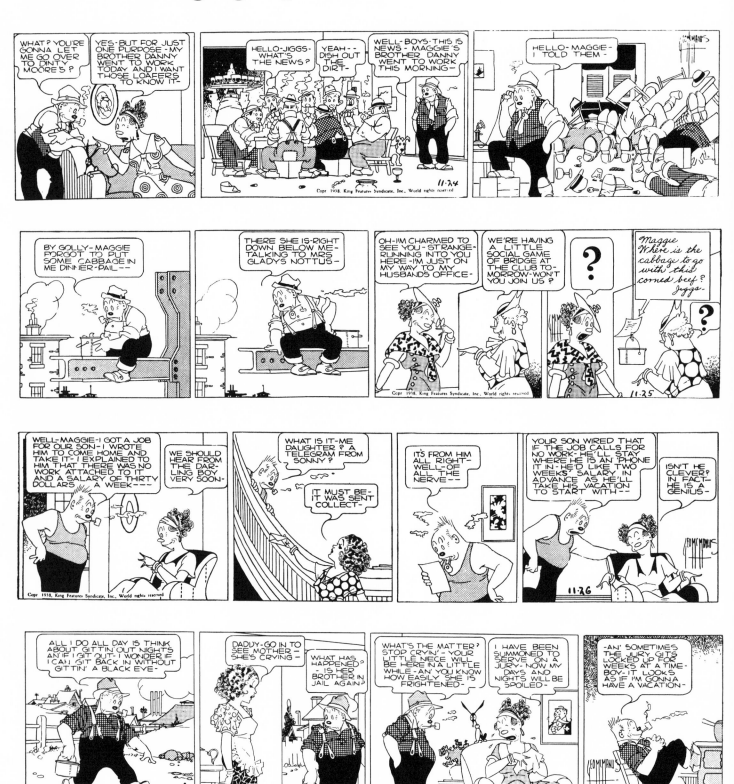

1938 ...Bringing Up Father

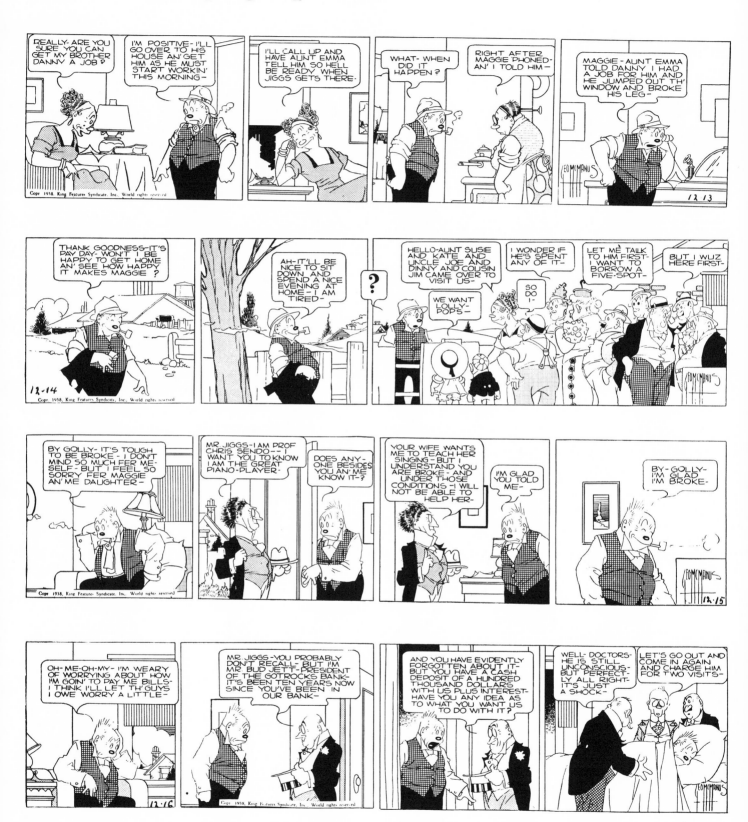

1939...Bringing Up Father

Bringing Up Father...1939

1939 ...Bringing Up Father

1939 ... Bringing Up Father

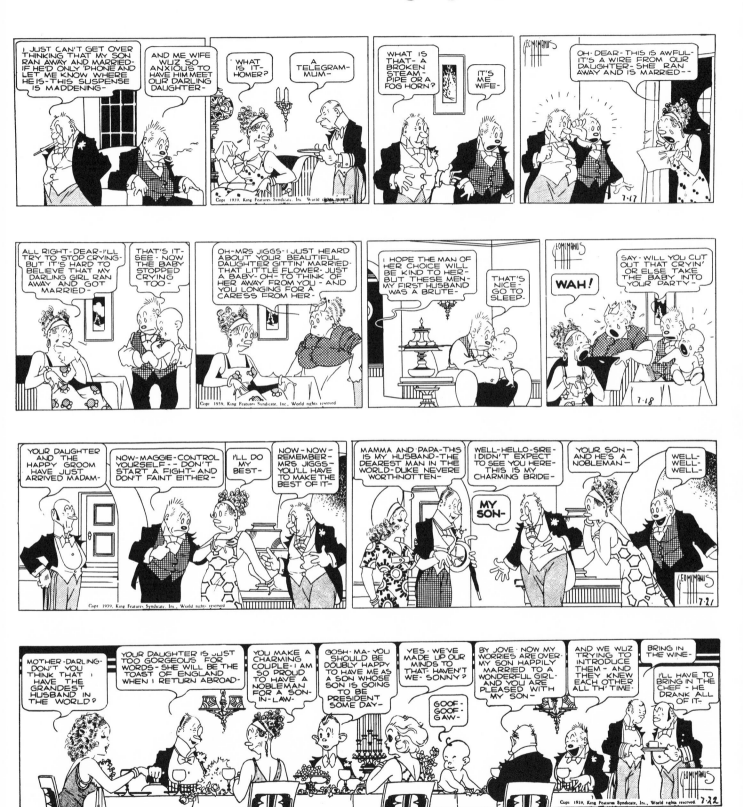

1939...Bringing Up Father

1939 ... Bringing Up Father

 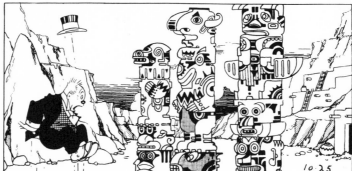 

1939 ... Bringing Up Father

1939 . . . Bringing Up Father

1940 ... Bringing Up Father

1940 ...Bringing Up Father

1940 ... Bringing Up Father

AH-MY VISIT TO WASHINGTON IS COMPLETE-I'VE SEEN THE PRESIDENT GO BY IN HIS CAR-

MAGGIE-I'D LIKE TO KNOW IF I KIN GO OUT-

SHUT UP-I WANT TO BE ALONE WITH MY THOUGHTS - I MUST WRITE SOME LETTERS TO MY FRIENDS -

JUST THINK-I SAW THE PRESIDENT-AM I THRILLED -

3·14

LISTEN-DAUGHTER-WILL YOU ASK MAGGIE IF I KIN GO OUT? SHE WON'T TALK TO ME - I MUST GET OUT-AS PRESIDENT ROOSEVELT REQUESTED ME TO CALL ON HIM AT THE WHITE HOUSE-

WHAT?

1940 ...Bringing Up Father

8·13

1941 ... Bringing Up Father

1942 ... Bringing Up Father

1942 ...Bringing Up Father

WHAT ARE ALL THOSE PEOPLE DOIN' IN THE PARLOR?

THEY ARE FROM THE FUR SHOP- MOTHER IS BUYING SOME FURS FOR HERSELF- AND-DADDY-I WILL BE NEEDING SOME PRETTY SOON-MYSELF-

WELL- I'LL PUT A STOP TO THAT- THESE ARE NOT DAYS TO BE BUYING LUXURIES-

!

WHAT DO YOU MEAN BY HAVING CUFFS ON YOUR TROUSERS??? DON'T YOU KNOW WE MUST CONSERVE ??

?

6-25

?

HE MARRIED A VILLAGE BELLE- AND SHE RANG HIS NECK!

1942 ...Bringing Up Father

1943 ... Bringing Up Father

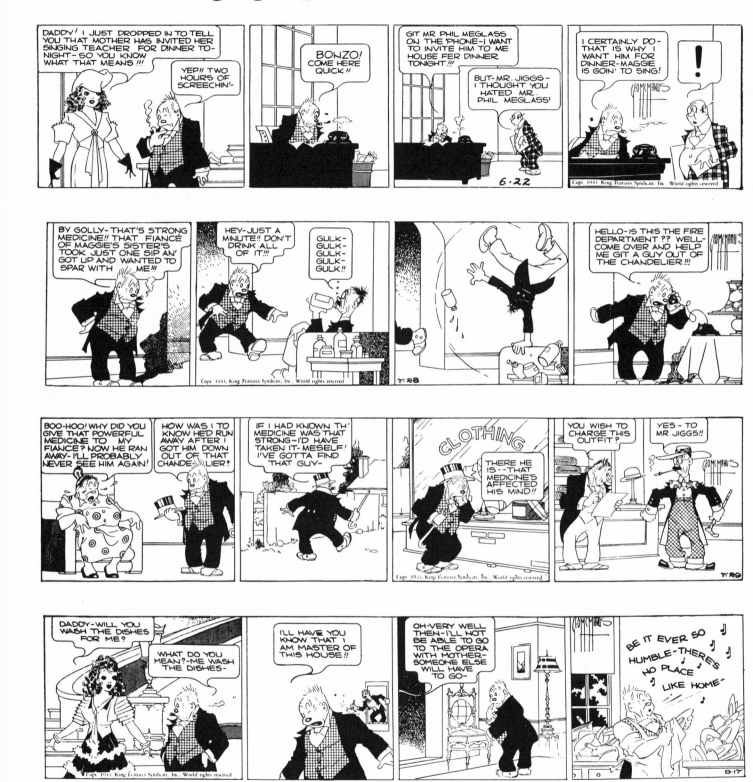

1944 ... Bringing Up Father

OH-GEE-I CAN'T GO TO THE GROCERY FOR YOU-I CAN'T WALK--MY FEET ARE TOO SORE !!!

WELL-YOU CAN TAKE THE CAR!

OH-FINE- AN' CAN I CALL AT, A FRIENDS HOUSE?

Copr. 1944, King Features Syndicate, Inc., World rights reserved.

12-1

MR JIGGS-WILL YOU SHOW ME HOW TO USE THIS VACUUM CLEANER ??

WHY CERTAINLY!

YOU JUST PUSH IT AROUND LIKE THIS-- AN' TO GET IN THE CORNERS-YOU JUST GET IN THE CORNERS!

AND YOU JUST GO OVER THE CARPET ONCE-BE CAREFUL NOT TO BUMP INTO THE FURNITURE!!

12-2

BE SURE TO EMPTY THE DUST SACK WHEN IT'S FULL-

Copr. 1944, King Features Syndicate, Inc., World rights reserved.

BOBBY-WHEN I WUZ A KID WE LIKED TO DANCE LIKE YOU KIDS DO-AN' VERY FEW OF US EVER WENT TO A DANCIN' SCHOOL--

WE LEARNED HOW TO DANCE WHEN WE GOT DRESSED UP SUNDAYS AND TH' OTHER KIDS IN TH' NEIGHBORHOOD WOULD SEE US--

Copr. 1944, King Features Syndicate, Inc., World rights reserved.

12-4

AND WE GOT OUR LESSONS FREE ON THE SIDEWALKS -AN' WE COULD ALWAYS GET A BIG PLATE OF ICE CREAM FOR A NICKEL -BUT NO ONE HAD A NICKEL !!!

IN THE OLDEN DAYS- GENTLEMEN ALWAYS GOT UP IN A CAR TO GIVE A LADY A SEAT ---

SOMETIMES FOUR OF THEM HAD TO GET UP ---

ALL THE BEAUTY PARLOR WORK WAS DONE AT HOME- OUT THE BACK WINDOW--

AND WE KIDS THOUGHT WE WERE HAVING A GOOD TIME IF OUR DADDY TOOK US TO THE DEPOT TO SEE A TRAIN PASS BY

SPDORK

12-5

Copr. 1944, King Features Syndicate, Inc., World rights reserved.

-AND SEVERE PUNISHMENT AT SCHOOL WAS TO HAVE TO SIT NEXT TO A GIRL-

1944 ... Bringing Up Father

FATHER WOULDN'T STRIKE ANY OF US KIDS - ONLY IN SELF-DEFENSE -

EVERY GIRL WANTED TO GROW UP AN' BE AN ACTRESS-BUT ALL THEY DID WAS GROW UP.

AND WE ALWAYS RAN TO MEET DADDY WHEN HE CAME HOME FROM WORK ESPECIALLY ON SATURDAY-

AN' IF ANY ONE HAD AN IRON DEER ON THEIR LAWN AND RODE IN A HANSOM CAB - THEY WERE RICH!

THERE WAS ALWAYS A KID IN THE NEIGHBORHOOD WHOSE PARENTS THOUGHT SHE HAD TALENT - - BUT THEY WERE ALONE IN THEIR THOUGHTS -

I HAD A LOT OF DISTANT RELATIVES-BECAUSE I MOVED OUT OF TOWN TO GET AWAY FROM THEM-

PARENTS SPENT DAYS AND DAYS TEACHING YOU TO TALK WHEN WE WERE BABIES - - THEN WE GREW UP AND THEY WOULDN'T LET YOU SAY ANYTHING -
SHUT UP!

GRANDMA IN THE OLDEN DAYS RETIRED AT EIGHT O'CLOCK IN THE EVENING NOW! YOU HAVE TO GO OUT LOOKING FOR HER AT TWELVE -

IN THE OLDEN DAYS TH' JIG WAS POPULAR-EXCEPT TO TH' PEOPLE DOWNSTAIRS.

TH' DANCES ALL WERE SLOW IN MOVEMENT- AND NO WONDER-

DANCING WAS POPULAR- BUT NOT ALL THE DANCERS -

SOME DANCERS WERE VERY LIGHT ON THEIR FEET AND JUST AS LIGHT IN THE HEAD!!

AND WE KIDS WENT TO BED WHEN WE WERE ORDERED TO- IN FACT-WE WERE GLAD TO- TO KEEP FROM FREEZING TO DEATH -

AND THE MINUTE WE HEARD MOTHER CALL- WE'D COME HOME OR KNOW WHY --
WILL-LEE!

IT TOOK US KIDS THREE HOURS TO GET FROM OUR HOMES TO THE SCHOOL- BUT WE COULD GET BACK IN TEN MINUTES-

WE NEVER KNEW MUCH AS SCHOLARS IN SCHOOL- AND NEITHER DID THE PRINCIPAL -

166

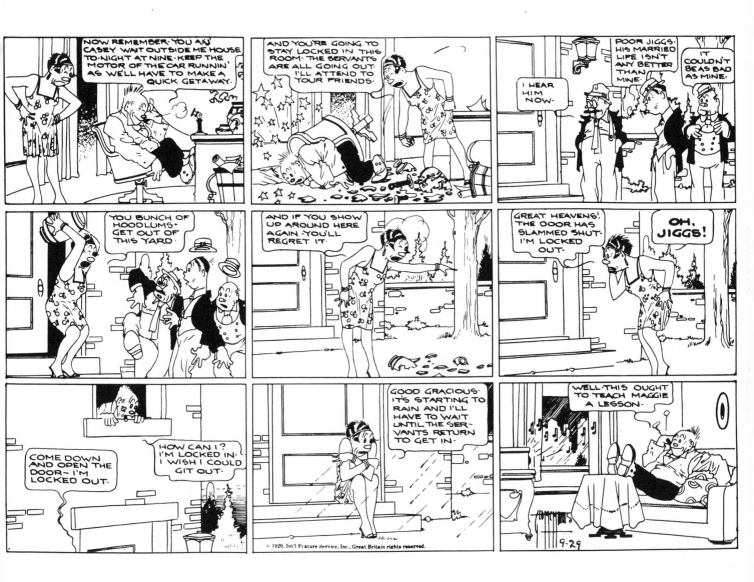

Bringing Up Father

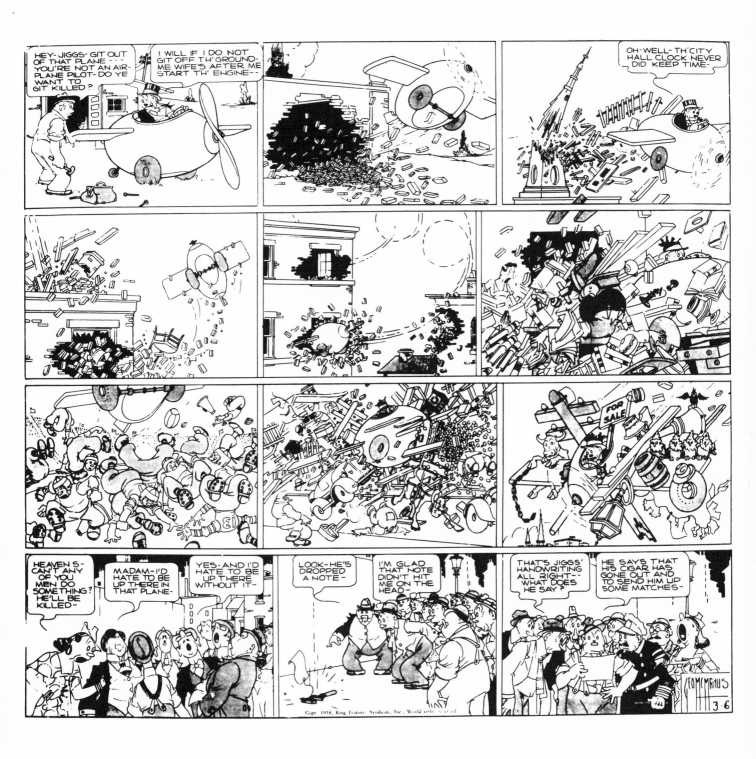

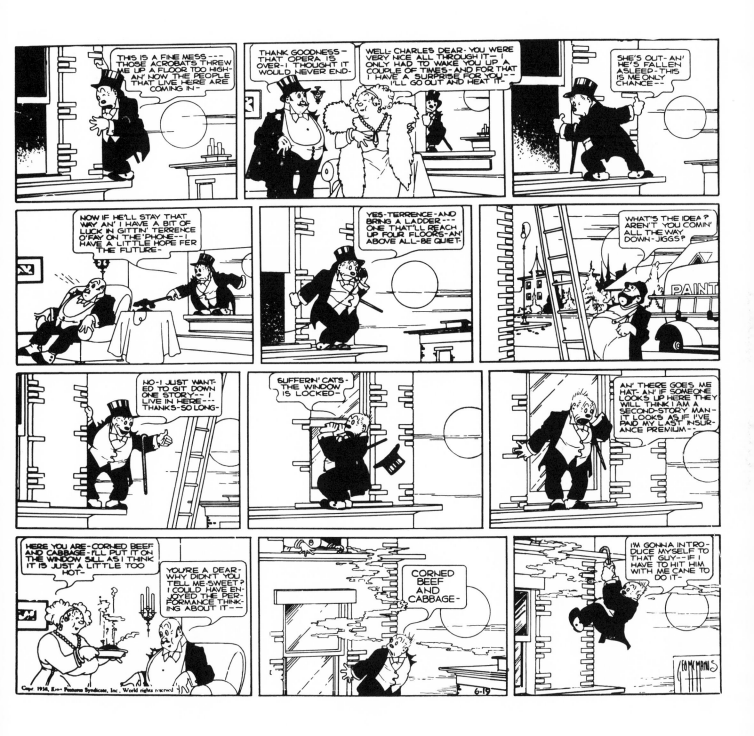

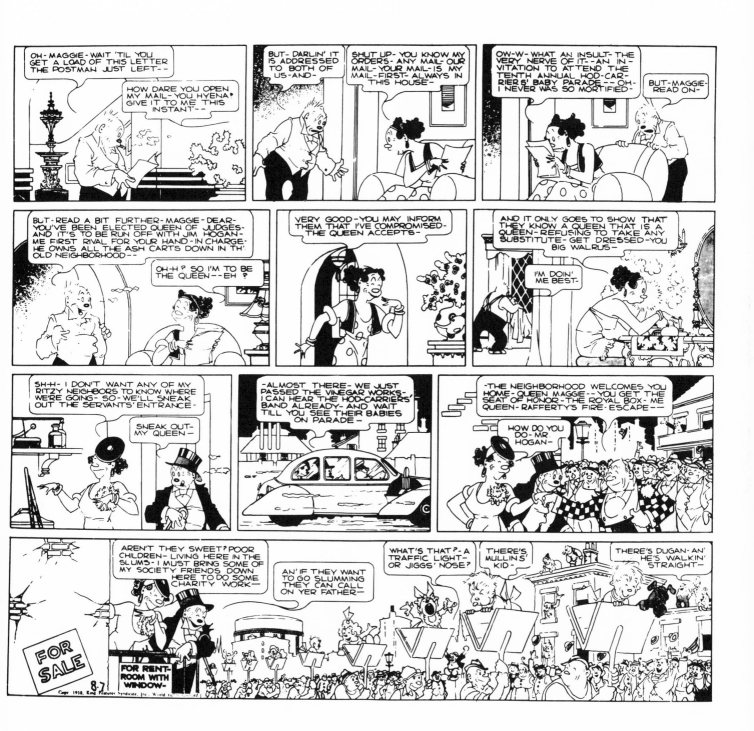

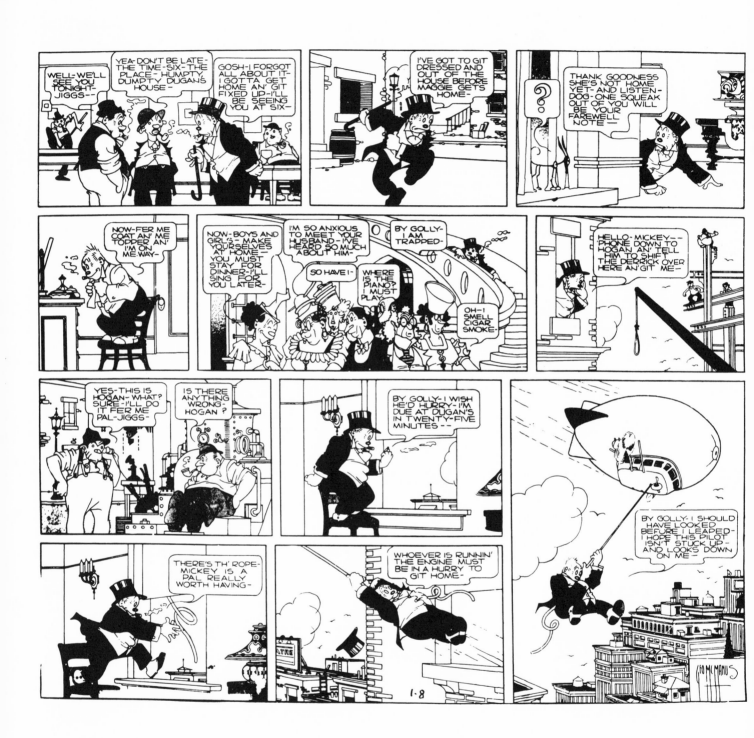

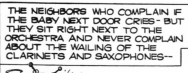

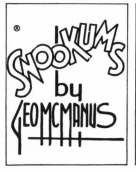

179